# THE LONG SECRET LIST OF THE WORLD'S WORST TOMB HUNTER

SCRIBO

First published in Great Britain by Scribo MMXIX
Scribo, an imprint of
The Salariya Book Company
25 Marlborough Place, Brighton, BN1 1UB

ISBN 978-1-912537-44-0

Book Design by David Salariya

Printed and bound in China

The text for this book is set in Century Schoolbook
The display type is Jacob Riley

# www.salariya.com

Artwork Credits
Illustrations: Isobel Lundie

# THE LONG-LOST SECRET DIARY OF THE WORLD'S WORST TOMB HUNTER

Written by
**Tim Collins**

Illustrated by
**Isobel Lundie**

SCRIBO
*a* SALARIYA *imprint*

# Chapter I

—

# Egypt, 1922

## Monday September 4ᵗʰ

Last night I went to sleep hoping for something to make my job exciting again. It seems my wish has come true.

Don't get me wrong. It's not that I dislike photographing rich tourists in front of the temple here in Luxor. It's just that it can feel like the same day over and over again.

I have to ask the tourists to keep still and look at the camera. Then my boss Ibrahim takes the shot, and one of the group will remember they want to remove their hat or eyeglasses and we'll have to start again so we don't end up with a blurry mess that's no use to anyone.

Then I rush back to the darkroom in Ibrahim's house to develop the prints and then dart back to the temple to sell them to the visitors.

But that's not what happened today.

A British man with a wide hat and a moustache approached us. He seemed to be in a hurry, and had sandy marks on his sleeves and trousers. He didn't look like the sort of tourist who'd just stepped off the paddle steamer, so my hopes were high that something different was on the cards.

That turned out to be right. The man was called Howard Carter and he's one of those archaeologists who dig in the valley across the river, looking for the tombs of ancient kings.

He wanted us to work with him for the next few weeks, taking pictures of all his wonderful finds.

Ibrahim wasn't sure. He was worried that someone might set up a rival photography business and steal our regular work around the temple. But I talked him round.

Mr Carter is convinced he's about to find a horde of ancient treasure. If that's true, we could take some fantastic pictures that people all around the world would want to see. And they could make us more money than a million shots of travellers outside the temple.

This last point is the one that convinced Ibrahim. So tomorrow after dawn prayer, we'll take a boat across the river and then continue to the site by donkey.

It will be good to photograph something other than tourists for a while. And at least dead kings will keep still when you tell them to.

*Tuesday September 5*[th]

Okay, so we haven't seen much in terms of kings or treasure so far. Mr Carter's site turned out to be a huge dusty pit at the side of the valley. He paced around and watched as his team dug up rubble and sifted it through sieves.

We waited in the shade of an overhanging cliff and set up our camera. But there wasn't much for us to do.

It was disappointing. But I think I need to be more patient. Mr Carter has waited years for a discovery, and he finally feels like he's getting close. The least I can do is wait a few days.

When I got home I told Mum and Dad I'd had a fantastic day. I always say that, whether things have been good or bad.

Dad thinks I should go and work with him in the Winter Palace hotel instead of messing around with cameras. He doesn't think photography is a proper job, and he can't see what a great opportunity Ibrahim is giving me.

If I ever complain about work to him, he takes the chance to lecture me about changing careers, so I always keep it to myself.

## GET REAL

*Howard Carter was born in London in 1874. At the age of 17, he travelled to Egypt to copy the decorations on tombs. He loved the country, dedicating his life to searching for the resting places of the ancient pharaohs.*

### Wednesday September 6th

There is still nothing for us to photograph. Ibrahim tried to take a shot of Mr Carter standing in front of the site, but he kept glancing over his shoulder instead of looking at us. He was as bad as one of those tourists.

I finally managed to keep Mr Carter's attention by asking about his work. This time he focused on me, looking the right way long enough for Ibrahim to take the picture.

*12*

He told me all about his epic search for the tomb of a king called Tutankhamun.

A few years ago, some other archaeologists found objects with Tutankhamun's name on in a small pit. They thought this was all that was left of Tutankhamun's tomb, but Mr Carter doesn't agree. He thinks the real tomb is still hidden under the ground somewhere.

Now he's convinced he's found the right spot. He's tried lots of other places, and thinks the current site is the last place the tomb could be.

What if he's wrong? It will mean he's spent his whole life searching for something that doesn't exist. But if he's right, he'll be remembered as one of the greatest archaeologists ever. It's quite a gamble.

It makes me glad I've chosen to be a photographer and not something like that. Sometimes we have bad days when sand blows into our cameras and we have to spend hours cleaning them at Ibrahim's house. But we're soon ready to go again.

If this dig doesn't work out, Mr Carter will have pretty much wasted his life. No wonder he looks so stressed.

## GET REAL

*Fifteen years earlier, in 1907, a team of archaeologists funded by an American lawyer called Theodore Davis discovered a pit containing several ancient jars. Inside one was a scrap of linen with Tutankhamun's name on it. This made Davis believe he had found Tutankhamun's tomb.*

## Thursday September 7<sup>th</sup>

Today we wandered around the valley and photographed some of the tombs that have already been discovered.

Ibrahim let me set up his Brownie Box camera and take the shots, which was a nice change. He usually does it all himself, because he says we're in too much of a hurry. But I can do it just as quickly as him.

I tried my best every time, making sure the camera was in exactly the right place to get the best light.

Then we went back to Luxor and developed the photographs in the darkroom in Ibrahim's house. I was quite pleased with them, and for once Ibrahim was happy about them too. He's even offered to frame one of some ancient workmen's huts and hang it in his corridor.

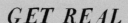
## GET REAL

*The Brownie box camera was launched in 1900 and became incredibly popular, as it was cheap to buy and easy to operate. In the days before digital photography, pictures were taken on rolls of film that were loaded into the camera. The film was then taken to a 'darkroom', which was lit just by red or green light. It would be passed through a series of chemicals to create 'negatives' which could then be used to create the photographs themselves, known as 'prints'.*

## Friday September 8th

We didn't go to the site until after we'd been to our local mosque for Friday prayers today. Mr Carter's team don't work on Fridays, but he was there on his own anyway.

I asked him if he ever took a day off, and he got angry. He said he was on the verge of a major discovery, and it would be irresponsible to lounge around when he could be checking progress on the site.

Even while the workers are away, he needs to survey the dig and decide where to place everyone the following week.

This was our busiest day yet, even though nothing has been found yet. Mr Carter wanted us to photograph the pit from every possible angle so he could study the prints.

He told us more about Tutankhamun as we worked, though it was a little harder to follow this time. Tutankhamun was a pharaoh, which means he was a king, but the word itself means 'great house'. And he was really called 'Tutankhaten', but he changed his name. And just to make it even more confusing, he actually had five different names in total, which Mr Carter went on to list.

I can't work out if Mr Carter is a genius or a crazy English man who spouts gibberish while staring at rocks.

At first I believed he really was on the verge of finding Tutankhamun's tomb, but now I'm not so sure. He doesn't have any real evidence – he's just looked over his massive piles of notes and diagrams and convinced himself that there's nowhere else it could be.

But he might be wrong. Those other archaeologists might have been right when they thought they'd already found everything. Maybe all that's left of Tutankhamun's possessions are those jars, and robbers took everything else centuries ago.

I know what Ibrahim thinks, because he wants me to take over this project on my own from next week. He'll go back to Luxor Temple and get more work from tourists while I stay out here.

He kept talking up what a great opportunity it was, but I could tell it was really because he doesn't think Mr Carter will find anything. He's decided that staying here will mean setting out at dawn from Luxor every morning just to photograph holes from a million different angles.

If he thought there was a chance of being around for a glorious discovery, he wouldn't abandon the dig.

## GET REAL

*Tutankhamun was originally known as Tutankhaten, meaning he was the living image of the god Aten. He changed his name when he began to worship the god Amun instead. Like all pharaohs, Tutankhamun had a total of five different names.*

# Chapter 2

## Lord Carnarvon

## Saturday September 9ᵗʰ

A tall British man visited the site in a motorcar today. Mr Carter and his team swarmed around him, so I knew he must be important. It turned out he was Lord Carnarvon, the 'sponsor' of the dig. This means he's paying for the whole thing, so it's no wonder everyone fawned over him.

Lord Carnarvon looked a few years older than Mr Carter and had a bigger moustache and an even wider hat. Maybe that's how they measure importance over in Britain. Their king probably has a hat and moustache that jut out for miles on either side.

Mr Carter is usually pretty grumpy, but he spent today following Lord Carnarvon around with a grin fixed on his face and his shoulders bowed.

Ibrahim said that the British are like donkeys. Not because they're good at carrying things, or because they leave their poo in piles at the side of the road, but because they nod up and kick down.

They instantly know from someone's voice and clothes whether they're above or below them, and they're nice or nasty accordingly.

This might be true of some British people, but I think Ibrahim is being unfair to Mr Carter.

He might put on a smile for Lord Carnarvon, but I don't think he cares about anyone living. The only people he really looks up to have been dead for thousands of years.

### *GET REAL*

*Searching for tombs was expensive, and archaeologists like Howard Carter needed help from rich patrons. In 1907 Howard Carter teamed up with Lord Carnarvon, a wealthy English aristocrat. A car accident had left Lord Carnarvon with serious health problems, and his doctors advised him not to spend winters in Britain. He went to Egypt for the climate, and soon became hooked on archaeology.*

## Sunday September 10th

Mr Carter and Lord Carnarvon had a massive argument today. The British version of having a massive argument involves people staying perfectly still and raising their voices, rather than yelling and hitting each other with sticks. But it still gave the whole dig an awkward atmosphere and everyone stopped working to stare at them.

I told Ibrahim he was wrong about Mr Carter. If he were a donkey, he'd be a grumpy one who refuses to budge and brays angrily at its owner.

Lord Carnarvon soon left in his motorcar, and Mr Carter yelled at everyone to get back to work.

After a while I went over to try to find out what had gone on.

Mr Carter said that Lord Carnarvon wanted to stop the dig. He said it had gone on too long without a result, and he'd wasted too much money.

Mr Carter told Lord Carnarvon he was so sure he'd discover something that he was willing to pay for the dig with his own savings. In the end Lord Carnarvon agreed to continue the funding, but only for a few more months. If Mr Carter doesn't find something soon, it will all be over.

No wonder he looked so worried. The search that has taken up so many years of his life could be about to end in failure.

I asked him why he was so obsessed with digging up someone who had been dead for three thousand years and if it wouldn't be just as good to dig up thirty people who'd been dead for a hundred years.

He looked at me as if I'd just knocked off his hat and tweaked his moustache. I suppose it was a silly question.

He said it wasn't just about Tutankhamun's corpse, but all the stuff that would be with it. He said that the pharaohs were buried with valuable possessions like jewellery, clothing, weapons and other things they thought would be useful in the afterlife. We could learn a lot about their era if we could find these objects.

Most tombs were robbed by ancient thieves, even though they were meant to be sacred places. But if Tutankhamun's tomb is intact, it will be one of the most valuable discoveries ever.

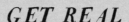

## GET REAL

*The ancient Egyptians believed that their pharaoh was the son of the great sun god. They thought that when he died, he'd be reunited with his father and enjoy a glorious afterlife. To ensure that the bodies of their kings were preserved, they built huge structures known as pyramids. Later, they switched to burying their kings in huge tombs cut deep into the rock near the city of Thebes. This area is now called the 'Valley of the Kings'.*

## Monday September 11ᵗʰ

Today was my first day on the site without Ibrahim, and Mr Carter announced that he'd made a discovery as soon as I arrived.

Visions of gleaming jewels ran through my mind, and I thought of all the fun I'd have boasting to Ibrahim about what he'd missed.

The reality was less exciting. Mr Carter pointed to a sickle he'd unearthed, with a wooden handle and stone blade. I had to photograph it from every angle while he made notes and measurements. He said a good archaeologist will study an object for hours in the ground rather than grabbing it straight away with their clumsy fingers.

You need to know where it was in relation to other finds so you can date it properly, and you need to treat it carefully with preservatives if you want to get it out of the ground intact.

It wasn't until late in the afternoon that Mr Carter finally removed the sickle. It came away without crumbling apart, and he said that

*30*

any museum would be glad to have it. Maybe, though I doubt they'd need to extend their opening hours.

I want to find the sort of treasure that would make a pirate jealous, not a rotting piece of wood and stone.

## Wednesday September 13th

I'm over it now, but today I made myself ill by spending too long in the sun.

Mr Carter didn't ask for me all morning, so I wandered around the valley again. This time I forgot to keep in the shade, and I didn't even bring my water bottle. Stupid, I know.

I started to feel light-headed and my legs went wobbly. I stopped to steady myself, and then I saw it.

31

A vision of a golden face appeared before me, so bright it was blinding. I closed my eyes, opened them again, and it was gone. All I could see was the sun shining on the rocks ahead.

I can see now what must have happened. I got myself in a confused state, and I mistook the reflection of the sun on the mountainside for a golden face.

But at the time I was convinced it was some sort of sign telling me where a tomb was. I can't remember exactly why. I wasn't thinking straight.

But I'm back home now, and I've had plenty to drink. I've taken my sleeping mat out onto the flat roof of our house, and the cool night air is making me feel much better.

## *Thursday September 14th*

Lord Carnarvon came back today, and if anything, he was even more cross. I watched Mr Carter lead him around, pointing at various parts of the site. He showed him the sickle, but he wasn't very impressed.

It's fair enough. With all the money Lord Carnarvon has put into the dig, he wants something more than a broken farming tool to show for it.

Mr Carter also tried showing him some of the photographs that I'd taken, but he shoved them aside angrily.

I was worried he might tell Mr Carter he was pulling the plug even sooner than planned, and I felt like running up and telling them about the golden face I saw. But what difference would it have made? All it proves is that I forgot to drink enough water.

Yet I am starting to believe there's something out here and we could find it, given enough time.

## Friday September 15<sup>th</sup>

I went to Friday prayers with Dad today and tried to tell him about the dig. It takes us ten minutes to walk from our house to the mosque, and I thought it would be a good chance to explain what's been going on. But instead of listening, he gave me a speech about how tomb-hunting was just another of my fads and I should concentrate on one thing rather than jumping around between interests.

This was very unfair. Photography and Tutankhamun are the only two things that

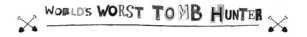

have ever really excited me. It's not like I change my ambition every day.

I found it hard to concentrate on the sermon when we were in the mosque because I was still thinking about the golden face. I wanted to tell someone about it, but I knew Dad wouldn't listen.

I went round to Ibrahim's house afterwards and tried to tell him instead. But right away he started talking about how weird Mr Carter and Lord Carnarvon were for obsessing over the distant past, so I couldn't tell him either.

In the end I found a stray cat and told it about the face. It mewed at me as if it understood, then led me down the street, turning at every corner to see if I was still following.

I wondered if the spirit of Tutankhamun had

entered the animal, and it would lead me to the true site of his hidden tomb.

I raced after the cat until I finally saw where it was taking me. It was the local butcher's shop. It's not the freshest place I've ever been to, but I doubt even they have anything over three thousand years old.

*Thanks a lot, cat!*

Stupid animal. I don't know why the ancients loved them so much.

## GET REAL

*Cats were held in high regard in ancient Egypt. A cat-headed goddess called Bastet was worshipped, mummified feline remains have been found in tiny coffins, and according to the Greek historian Herodotus, Egyptians would shave their eyebrows as a sign of mourning when their pet cats died. If they'd had YouTube, they'd probably have spent almost as much time watching 'FUNNIEST CAT VIDEOS EVER' compilations as we do.*

# Chapter 3

## Working on the dig

## Saturday September 16th

Mr Carter seemed even grumpier than usual when I arrived today. It took me a while to get the news out of him, and it wasn't good.

It turns out they don't want me around anymore. Lord Carnarvon has told Mr Carter to find ways of keeping the budget down, so he's cutting out photography.

I wished him luck and set off for home. I was more upset about it than I had any right to be. He promised to fetch me when he finds the tomb, and I'm sure he's telling the truth.

It's just that I want to be there at the moment he discovers something. I don't want to hear about it from other people, I want to see it.

## Sunday September 17th

I went back to Ibrahim today and told him I wasn't needed on the dig anymore. He said he wasn't surprised, but it was a shame about the money. I helped him develop some more tourist photographs, but my mind was still on the dig.

## Tuesday September 19th

I haven't been able to stop thinking about the dig, and today I decided to do something about it.

I asked Ibrahim if I could start leaving early to go and help Mr Carter. He couldn't understand why I'd want to trek out to that hot, dusty site every day. I couldn't bring myself to tell him about the golden face, so I just said I had a strong feeling that Mr Carter was about to find something.

Ibrahim only agreed after I promised Mr Carter wasn't paying me anything. And he doesn't want me to do any photography for free, either. But that's okay. I'll help out in any way I can. I'll tunnel into the mountains with my fingers if Mr Carter wants. I just need to be there.

I couldn't tell Dad, obviously. He'd have taken it as proof that I'm flitting between different interests instead of sticking with one thing. So I just told him we were really busy and I'd need to work late with Ibrahim every night.

### *Wednesday September 20th*

I left work at five and trekked over to the dig. Mr Carter was examining another sickle when I got there, and it took ages to get his attention and ask how I could help.

He pointed at the far-left corner of the site without taking his eyes off the artefact.

I was hoping for clearer instructions, but I didn't want to push my luck. Maybe if I'd had his full attention, he'd have realised I wasn't qualified to join his excavation and told me to go away.

I stumbled across uneven stretches of ground, weaving around the clouds of dust that Mr Carter's team were sending up.

The corner of the dig was deeper than the rest and I found myself out of sight of all the others, in a pit that went far below the sand to the hard rock underneath. I pressed the solid ground, wondering how I was meant to break it up.

There was a small trowel behind me, so I thought I'd give that a try.

Jabbing the ground with it didn't have much impact. I did it harder, but still nothing happened. So I lifted the trowel up, then slammed it down with all my strength.

This time something happened. The trowel broke in two. The wooden handle snapped away and split in half.

*45*

It was at this point that I noticed there was also a pickaxe behind me. Whoops. So that was how I should have got into the hard ground.

I switched to this other tool and it got much easier. I kept going for hours, smacking it into the ground and pulling away the hard lumps.

It was only as the light began to fade that I wondered what I was going to do with the trowel. At first I thought I'd bury it. But then I remembered Mr Carter was so desperate for success he'd probably dig it up and convince himself he'd found Tutankhamun's personal gardening tool.

I decided it would be better to own up, so I handed the two pieces over to Mr Carter as I left. I was hoping he'd still be so distracted by the sickle that he wouldn't say anything, but

he went into a big rant about how we couldn't afford to keep buying new tools now that Lord Carnarvon was cutting the budget.

I thought he was going to tell me to keep away, but he didn't. He was probably so stressed about time running out that he'd forgotten no one had invited me in the first place.

### *Thursday September 21st*
Another day of work followed by another evening on the dig.

By the time I got home I was exhausted and covered in sand. Mum and Dad asked me how I'd got so dirty taking photographs. I said there'd been a fierce sandstorm at the temple, but they weren't convinced. Dad said he hadn't noticed anything like that from the hotel.

I sat down while Mum and Dad went to get me some bread and fava beans. As soon as I did so, my eyelids began to feel heavy, and my rickety wooden chair seemed surprisingly comfortable. A moment later I opened my eyes to see Mum pacing up and down above me. I'd got so comfy that I'd fallen asleep and slid onto the floor.

Mum was yelling that Ibrahim must be overworking me and that she was going round to his house right away to get him to double my pay.

I had no choice but to own up. I told them I was helping Mr Carter in the evenings, and not because he was paying me, but because I was desperate to find Tutankhamun. I told them I was sure the pharaoh was out there, and we were running out of time to find him.

Dad tried to reel off his lecture about how I should stick with one interest rather than

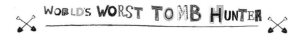 

changing all the time, but Mum interrupted him. She said finding Tutankhamun obviously meant a lot to me, and I should keep going out to help Mr Carter.

Surprisingly, Dad agreed. I am officially allowed to go to the dig. Now all I have to do is find a way to actually help rather than make things worse.

## Friday September 22nd

I went back to the site after Friday prayers again today. Mr Carter was scrabbling around in one of the deep pits, so I climbed down the rope and joined him.

I asked him why the ancient kings went to all the effort of burying themselves so deep in the rocks. If they were already dead, why did they need to protect themselves?

Mr Carter said they believed the body was the home of their life force or 'ka', and it needed to be preserved after death. As well as tunnelling deep into the ground, they'd treat bodies to stop them decaying. They'd take out the lungs, stomach, intestines and liver and put them in jars, but leave the heart so it could be judged by the jackal-headed god Anubis. Then they'd dry the bodies, rub oil into them and wrap them in bandages.

That sounds like a pretty disgusting job. Whenever I'm photographing rich tourists who won't keep still, I'll have to remind myself that at least I don't have to remove smelly royal innards and massage oil into their dead flesh.

## GET REAL

*The ancient Egyptians believed that a body had to be preserved for the afterlife. Their process of preparing and wrapping a body is known as 'mummification'. It took skilled embalmers weeks to transform a dead body into a mummy ready for burial. Our word 'mummy' derives from the Arabic word for bitumen, the thick black substance used in embalming. Disgustingly, in the Middle Ages, mummies were thought to have healing properties, and ground mummy was mixed into drinks to treat injuries like bruising.*

*Mummies are the most famous images from ancient Egypt, and used to be popular in horror films until everyone realised that they weren't very scary and would be easy to escape from even if you weren't that good at running.*

## Saturday September 23rd

There were no tourists at the temple this morning, so Ibrahim let me go to the dig right away. I thought I could be of more help to Mr Carter if I were there for longer, but this turned out to be wrong.

Mr Carter was working in the same pit, and he pointed to the area he wanted me to work

on. We were so deep down that it wasn't clear where he meant, but I climbed out and did my best to find the right place.

I glanced from side to side as I walked around. I should really have kept my eyes on the ground. After a few steps, I found myself tumbling down. One minute I was strolling across the site, the next I was sprawled at the bottom of another hole.

I got up and brushed the dust from my robe. I hadn't broken my leg or twisted my ankle. That was something. But I still had the embarrassment to cope with.

There was no one around the top of the pit, so I reckoned the others hadn't noticed. All I had to do was escape quietly and get on with my work.

Unlike Mr Carter's pit, this one didn't have a rope dangling into it. Whoever was working here must have taken it with them.

I tried to crawl up by digging my fingers into the soil, but I only managed to cover myself in hard clumps of sand.

I fumbled around the dark edges of the pit and found a long metal rake. Lifting it above my head, I found that it almost reached the top of the hole. If I could jump up and hook it into the ground, I might be able to clamber out.

I leapt up as high as I could and lunged the rake forward. Instead of hooking into the ground above me, it dislodged even more dirt.

It showered down on me, filling my eyes and nostrils, and I thought I was going to be buried alive. I couldn't stop myself from crying out.

By the time I was free of the horrible dust, I could see Mr Carter and four members of his team peering down at me and looking annoyed.

One of the workers lowered a rope into the pit and I finally manged to get out. I glanced down at the pit on the way up and saw the bottom was now full of rubble.

Not a great day, then. Not only did I achieve nothing, but I created extra work for the others. Amazingly, Mr Carter still hasn't banned me from going back.

### Sunday September 24th

I helped out on the dig again this evening. I soon spotted Mr Carter taking a break for some water, and I went over to speak to him.

Instead of asking him more about the distant past, I tried asking him about the future. In particular, I asked him what he'd do if he didn't find anything in our current spot.

I've been thinking about it quite a lot recently. Every day we dig deeper and still we find no tomb. So are we really in the right place? Mr Carter says he's tried everywhere else, but that can't be true. Tutankhamun might have chosen burial miles out into the desert for all we know.

As soon as I asked the question, I could tell it wasn't a good idea. Mr Carter's face went red, and he curled his fists into tight balls. I thought he was going to shout, but instead he almost whispered. He said failure was not an option, they would find something, they had to find something and they were in absolutely the right place.

Then he just turned and walked into the valley. I tried shouting after him to see if there was anything he wanted me to do, but he kept going.

I can't believe my simple question was enough to make him abandon us. He must be really worried about his chances of finding the tomb now.

I stuck around and did my best to help. One of the team came over to me and asked which part he should work on next. He must have assumed Mr Carter had put me in charge before going.

Maybe I should have told him to wait for Mr Carter to return, but I didn't think we should waste any digging time, so I pointed to an untouched stretch of land a few feet away from the site.

Soon more of the workers had moved on to this new section too. We didn't find Tutankhamun,

but at least we kept ourselves busy while Mr Carter was in a bad mood.

## *Monday September 25th*

Not a good day. I went straight to the dig after work again. I was expecting Mr Carter to apologise for his behaviour yesterday, but instead he blew his top.

He yelled at me for moving the dig to a bit of land he'd already searched.

I got angry at this point, which wasn't wise. But I didn't like the way Mr Carter was blaming me for his own mistakes. I shouted back at him, pointing out that he'd been digging in the same place for months and had found nothing, so maybe it was time to try somewhere new.

He pointed in the direction of Luxor and told me to go home and never return.

Oh well. I supposed I'd expected it after breaking the tool and getting stuck in that hole. But I was surprised it finally happened just when I thought I'd done well.

*Go home and stay there!*

# Chapter 4

## A new idea

## Tuesday September 26ᵗʰ

I went to Ibrahim's house today and told him
about Mr Carter's behaviour. He said it wasn't
surprising that someone obsessed with the
past was so weird because everyone in the past
was weird too. He said that they believed in
lots of different animal-headed gods instead of
worshipping Allah like we do. And he said they
did strange stuff like writing in pictures and
burying themselves with all their belongings.

Then he ran around the house giggling and
pointing out things I should put in his tomb when
he dies. It might happen sooner than he thinks if
he says any of this stuff in front of Mr Carter.

I didn't have the energy to argue back, but I
don't agree with Ibrahim. I know a lot of the
stuff they did back in the past seems odd to us,
but only because it was different. And who's

to say things will stay the way they are now forever?

Maybe in a hundred years, humans will be using pictures instead of words again. For all I know, they could invent some new system of sending smiling or sad faces to people to express their feelings. Who knows what will happen?

And I don't think Mr Carter was acting strangely for no reason. I think he knows the tomb isn't in the current site and he needs to try somewhere else, but he has no idea where that should be, and it's driving him mad.

He says everywhere else in the valley has been excavated before. Maybe it has. But he might as well switch to another place before time runs out.

In the afternoon, a British man wearing a black hat called round for Ibrahim, but had to

wait for him to finish in the darkroom. I found myself telling him all about the dig.

I was very honest about how disappointed I was, which was surprising. I'd only just met this man, and I don't usually open up to strangers. But he kept asking questions, and seemed trustworthy, so I went on talking.

At one point I said it felt like I was cursed, and he leapt up, shouting about what a great angle that was. I had no idea what he meant by 'angle', but there was no time to question him. He was reeling off this crazy story about Tutankhamun seeking revenge on me from beyond the grave because I sought to disturb his eternal slumber.

That wasn't what I was saying at all. I just meant things hadn't gone well on the dig. I wasn't saying I thought the dead pharaoh was going to rise from his grave and chase after me with his bandages dragging on the floor.

Ibrahim soon emerged from the darkroom and introduced me to the man, and everything became clear. The man's name is Mr Thompson and he's the Egyptian correspondent of *The Times* newspaper in London. He was waiting for some prints of the temple to send to his editor back there.

Mr Thompson didn't really believe all that nonsense about Tutankhamun getting revenge on me. He was just trying to think of a story that would excite his readers.

I thought about how annoyed Mr Carter would be if he thought I'd been spouting this nonsense, and I begged Mr Thompson not to run the story.

He said his editor wouldn't think it was dramatic enough yet, but if I died he might go for it. I told him I'd take extra care not to.

## GET REAL

*The ancient Egyptians used a form of writing called 'hieroglyphics', which was made up of small pictures. It was very complicated, with some of the pictures standing for objects and actions and others standing for sounds.*

### Wednesday September 27th

Ibrahim left me in the darkroom to develop some prints this morning. Spending all that time alone in the gloomy room made me think about Mr Carter and the dig. I still wanted to go back, but I really hadn't helped when I was there. Maybe the best thing would be to leave them alone to get on with it.

But I still had a feeling I could help him in some way. It was when I stepped out of the darkroom for lunch that it happened. For a brief moment, I saw the golden face again. The one that had appeared to me in the valley that day I forgot to drink.

I rubbed my eyes and looked again. All I had really seen was my own face reflected in one of the photographs Ibrahim had framed. The sun glinting off my face was so bright it had made it look golden.

I stepped closer to the picture and saw it was the
one I'd taken of the row of ancient workmen's
huts. Something about it bothered me, but
I couldn't work out what. Then I realised.
Mr Carter said everywhere in the Valley of
the Kings had been searched. But the place
underneath those huts couldn't have been,
because they'd been there for thousands of years.

For a moment, I was convinced I'd worked out
the real location of Tutankhamun's tomb. I felt
like abandoning Ibrahim's house, running back
to the dig and telling Mr Carter. But I didn't. I
still had work to do, and Mr Carter had made it
clear I wasn't welcome.

I'm sure it's a stupid idea anyway. I need
to focus on my work and forget about
Tutankhamun.

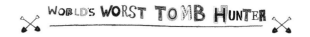

## *Thursday September 28ᵗʰ*

It's no use. I can't stop thinking about it. Those huts would be the ideal place to look. They're really near some of the other tombs, and if there's something underneath them it won't have been touched for centuries.

I want to tell Mr Carter about my idea, but how can I even approach him? If I go back he'll probably strike me with his pickaxe and Tutankhamun won't be the only one buried under the sand.

Maybe I'll try tomorrow after Friday prayers. His team will have the day off, and he'll be on his own again and more likely to listen. Either that or he'll think he's got more chance of getting away with killing me.

## Friday September 29th

Oh well. I tried my best. Mr Carter was in a deep trench on his own, just as I thought he'd be. I tried shouting at him, but he pointed to a rope and beckoned me down.

The rope strained and swayed as I struggled down. I was worried I'd pull it free and trap both of us down there, but it just about held.

When I was at the bottom, I explained my idea about the huts and Mr Carter nodded without frowning, shouting or murdering me. When I'd finished, he simply pointed down at the ground and said Tutankhamun was right there, probably just inches away. But his voice was thin and cracked. He sounded like he was trying to convince himself to avoid going insane.

I climbed back up the rope, leaving him in the hole he's quite literally dug himself into.

It looks like he's determined to keep going there until time runs out. He'll burrow to the other side of the world before admitting he's wrong.

### *Saturday September 30*th

I was in the darkroom this afternoon when Ibrahim called for me. He said there were two British men waiting to see me outside. I thought one might be Mr Carter, but I couldn't think who the other might be.

I rushed out to see Mr Carter standing next to Lord Carnarvon. Mr Carter made me repeat everything I'd said yesterday while Lord Carnarvon nodded.

I felt like I should probably bow or something while speaking to an English aristocrat, but I just gabbled about my theory as if he had no more money and castles than me.

After I'd finished, Lord Carnarvon asked how sure I was. They both kept their eyes fixed on me and I felt a sudden sense of responsibility. These men had dedicated their lives to this quest. This was their last chance and I didn't want to be the one who'd make them waste it.

On the other hand, I was pretty sure they weren't going to get anywhere with their current location. Why not persuade them to try one last roll of the dice?

I told them I was convinced. Lord Carnarvon nodded and announced he was moving the dig. He said I should come and work for them full-time, and Ibrahim agreed on the condition that I would be the only photographer allowed into the tomb when we found it.

They strolled away, looking pretty hopeful. Even Ibrahim was grinning, no doubt thinking about the money he could make from exclusive photographs.

The whole operation is moving deeper into the valley now, and it's all because of my hunch. I really hope it pays off.

### Sunday October 1st

I crossed the river just after dawn, hoping to get to the new site early and watch Mr Carter's team make a start. There are usually a few men with donkeys on the other side, but today there was just one.

An old man and a scrawny donkey were asleep beside the road. I didn't want to wake them up, so I decided to continue on foot.

Unfortunately, I tripped over a rock and slammed down to the ground, waking both the man and his animal. He pretty much demanded to take me to the site, and he seemed desperate for the business, so I had to agree.

I climbed on the animal's back and it was soon obvious why it didn't get much work.

The donkey took a few steps forward, then retreated. The old man yelled at it and tugged on its rope, but it just stepped back even further. I'd already been on the creature's back

for ten minutes, and I was further from the site than when I'd started.

The journey went on and on like this. The donkey would plod forward for a while, then stop to look at the ground. The man would shout at it, try and drag it forward, then go behind and push it, all to no avail.

I kept telling the old man that I'd rather walk, and I'd still pay him if he wanted, but he insisted on taking me. At one point, the stubborn creature even slumped down to the ground, almost tipping me off and setting me free. But the old man held me up while yelling at his animal.

By the time I made it to the site, Mr Carter's team had already made a start on dismantling the ancient huts.

Lord Carnarvon was sitting in the shade, but Mr Carter was zipping restlessly around.

I sat next to Lord Carnarvon and asked him how he'd got so interested in tombs. He said he'd come to Egypt to escape the cold English winters, and had taken up Egyptology to pass the time.

His first excavations failed to yield anything interesting, but when he started working with Mr Carter, things improved. They'd had a good run of success, but they still hadn't managed to find the thing they really wanted – Tutankhamun.

I told him we were close, and he said he admired my confidence.

The team made good progress, and we should be able to start digging soon. I left at dusk, and

luckily I didn't run into the old man and his donkey again, so it didn't take me long to get back.

## GET REAL

*Lord Carnarvon first employed Howard Carter to work on a site near Luxor in 1907. They were still working together in 1912 when Theodore Davis gave up on the Valley of the Kings, declaring that all the tombs had been discovered. Lord Carnarvon and Howard Carter were given permission to dig there instead, and they began their search for Tutankhamun.*

## Monday October 2nd

Lord Carnarvon's wife and daughter came
out to the site today, along with a huge crowd
of British people who were apparently their
servants. Lady Carnarvon wasn't exactly
dressed for a dig. She had a hat that was
wider than Mr Carter's and Lord Carnarvon's
combined, which means she must have been the
most important British person of all.

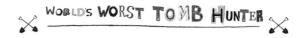

She was also wearing a thick black dress, a veil
to protect her face from the dust, and expensive
jewels that glinted in the sun.

She was already red and hot when she arrived,
and as the sun rose she turned almost purple.
One of Lady Carnarvon's servants wafted a fan
in front of her face, while a man in a thick black
jacket took her pulse. This man was her doctor,
though he didn't seem to know enough about
health to realise that taking his coat off might
be a good idea.

Another man in a heavy coat arrived soon
afterwards. I wondered if he was another
medical expert, but he turned out to be Lady
Carnarvon's cook, who had come all the way
from England with her.

Lady Carnarvon made everyone stop work
at eleven so she could eat some sandwiches

without any dust getting into them. They were made with white bread which had been cut into squares, and looked very different from the flatbread we have at home.

Lord Carnarvon tried to hurry her so he could carry on, but she snapped at him.

After Lady Carnarvon had finished her snack and the team could continue, she called me over and questioned me all about the old pharaohs. I only knew the answers from talking to Mr Carter, but she seemed to think everyone from Egypt would automatically know all about the distant past, like we still use hieroglyphics or something.

She nodded and said she was satisfied, as though I'd passed her test, and she went back to grumbling about the heat while her servants fanned her.

Can't somebody do something about this heat?

By contrast, their daughter Lady Evelyn looked like she was enjoying herself. She was wearing a light jacket and dress, as well as flat shoes. She grabbed Mr Carter by the hand and made him explain everything she pointed at. Clouds of dust billowed all around her, but she didn't seem to mind.

Lord Carnarvon and his family are travelling on to Cairo tomorrow, but we've promised to send a telegram and wait for them to return when we discover the tomb.

83

## Wednesday October 4th

We've found nothing yet. I spent this morning running around and tossing rocks about at random, but then Mr Carter assigned me a patch to work on. He said we'd only succeed through steady, patient work, and I know he's right. But I really want something to turn up soon. This was all my idea.

# Chapter 5

—

# Discovery!

## Wednesday November 8th

I looked up from my work last night to discover I was the only person left. The others had all gone while I'd been desperately scooping rubble away.

I put my tools down and sighed. It was time to start the long journey home.

I couldn't even get that right. I took a step forward and fell flat on my face. I couldn't bring myself to get up again for a while, so I just lay there, reflecting on how much things had gone wrong. We hadn't found the tomb, and I couldn't even walk away from the dig without tripping over a pickaxe.

Except that wasn't right. My pickaxe was right next to me, so I couldn't have stumbled on it.

I pushed myself up to see what had made me fall. There was a long, thin stone sticking out of the dust. It looked very unusual, and I was surprised I hadn't noticed it earlier.

I went over to examine it. Brushing the sand and rubble away, I saw it wasn't really a stone at all. It was a layer of hard rock that had been cut into a flat shape.

I felt my heart hammering in my chest as I realised what it was. It was a step. Someone had deliberately made a step. And if there was one step, there might be others. And if there were others, they might be leading to something.

Something like a tomb.

I grabbed my trowel and scooped the dirt away. The light was fading, the temperature was dipping and I was alone. But I had to know if I'd found something.

I kept going in a trance, unaware of the hunger and tiredness that would have driven me mad at any other time.

Eventually I uncovered another step. I'd been right. This was the top of a staircase.

Every now and then I heard a nagging voice telling me to go home and rest. Whatever these steps were, they'd still be there in the morning. But I couldn't stop myself.

It was frantic, disorganised work. I was dumping the debris around the hole, and sometimes the piles would collapse into it, meaning I'd have to take the same rocks out again.

But I still managed to uncover five steps by the time dawn broke.

I heard a gasp behind me and turned around to see Mr Carter. He was staring at my excavation with his mouth open and his moustache trembling.

At first he was too shocked to say anything, and could only crouch down and pat the steps one at a time.

Then he muttered that this was it, we'd found him at last, it had to be him, everything was finally paying off.

He scooped rubble away with his palms, working in the same haphazard way I'd been doing all night.

But when his team began to arrive, he snapped out of it, assigning them roles so we could clear the staircase as efficiently as possible.

Soon my little staircase was a blur of activity, and before long a narrow rectangular pit was emerging, with the steps at one end and a flat chunk of stone at the other, which Mr Carter said was the top of a doorway.

I was attempting to approach it when I felt a
weakness in my knees. The next thing I knew
I was looking up at Mr Carter and the others.
They'd all stopped work to gaze down at me,
still grasping their trowels and shovels.

They swayed above me in the midday sun. I
was so hot and confused I thought that I was
Tutankhamun himself, and that Mr Carter and
his team had just dug me out of my grave.

They gave me water, bundled me onto a
donkey and took me back home. I remember
murmuring something about how I was the
pharaoh and I commanded them to let me
return to my tomb.

Mum and Dad yelled at me when I got back
home. They were worried that I'd been away
all night, but I couldn't understand why. I was

the pharaoh and I was allowed to do whatever I wanted. But then I remembered that if I was pharaoh, it meant Dad was a god, so it would be better to stay on the right side of him. I apologised and collapsed onto my sleeping mat.

I woke up a couple of hours ago, just after nine in the evening. The confusion has now passed and I realise I am not, in fact, the pharaoh. But I might have just discovered one.

I really need to get back to the site. I can't stand to be away. I know Mr Carter says that patience is one of the greatest tools of the archaeologist, but we could be on the verge of something amazing here.

I'm going back right now.

No, I'm not.

I just tried leaving and Dad blocked the doorway. I told him I'd probably just made one of the greatest discoveries ever, but he thought I was still talking nonsense because of my exhaustion, and told me to go back to sleep.

So now I'm trapped in my room, wondering what's going on over at the dig.

### *Thursday November 9th*

This is terrible. It's all going on without me. Mr Carter and his team are opening the tomb and I'm not there to see it because the stupid doctor came round and said I have a fever and need to rest.

Why did I work through the night without food or water? The steps wouldn't have run away if I'd left them for a few hours.

I just got carried away. And now I'm missing the greatest discovery ever.

I know I'm not very well, but I think Mum and Dad should let me go back anyway. I helped to find the tomb. I need to be there.

## Friday November 10th

I tried to escape and return to the dig while Dad was out at Friday prayers. As soon as I was sure he'd gone, I rushed out. I managed about three steps before my legs began to wobble and I crashed down to the ground. Maybe the doctor was right about me needing time to recover.

95

## Sunday November 12ᵗʰ

I was lying on my sleeping mat this morning
when I saw Howard Carter appear in front
of me. At first I thought it might be a dream
brought on by my fever, but when he didn't
start flying or turn into one of my old teachers,
I realised he was really there.

He said that his team had cleared away the rubble and found a doorway blocked with a layer of stones covered in plaster. The good news is that there are seals stamped into it bearing Tutankhamun's name, so we know we've found the right place. The bad news is that part of the surface had been opened and resealed, probably by robbers, so there might not be much left inside.

And we won't find out for a while, either. Mr Carter doesn't want to open the tomb without Lord Carnarvon, who's currently in London. He's coming over, but it will take him two weeks.

That suits me. I'm bound to have recovered by then, so I know I'm not going to miss anything.

In the meantime, Mr Carter has refilled the stairwell and we need to keep it secret.

We don't want the authorities to know just yet, and we certainly don't want the press to find out. Mr Carter and Lord Carnarvon have been waiting years to find the tomb, and they want to open it in peace. I'll be allowed to join them, and so will Lady Evelyn, but no one else.

For now, all I have to do is drink lots of water, eat lots of bread and beans, get better and try to get through the next two weeks without driving myself mad by wondering what's inside.

*Monday November 13th*
My fever has passed now, so all I have to do is wait.

This is torture. Every time I look at the clock I expect hours to have passed, but find out

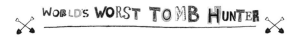 

that only minutes have gone by. What must it be like for Mr Carter? His whole life has been leading to this.

## GET REAL

*Travelling from England to Luxor wasn't easy in the 1920s. You'd take a boat to the port of Alexandria, continue to Cairo by train, then take a paddle steamer down the Nile. The whole journey would take around two weeks, while these days a flight would take just a few hours.*

### Tuesday November 14<sup>th</sup>

I can't stop thinking about that doorway. We know it was tampered with, so thieves must have been in. But how much did they take and how much did they leave? I wish Lord Carnarvon would hurry up and get here so we can find out.

## GET REAL

*The tombs of pharaohs were often robbed soon after the burials took place. It was likely to have been the builders of the tombs themselves who stole from them. They knew how to get to the most valuable items fast. They smashed shrines and coffins and rifled through chests to get to valuable things like gold, jewels, linen and glass.*

### Thursday November 16th

I was feeling restless today, so I went back to Ibrahim's house and asked if there was anything I could help with. I couldn't tell him we'd found the tomb, so I had to pretend I was taking a few days off because of sunstroke.

This meant I had to listen to him remind me that he'd told me it wouldn't end well if I meddled around with ancient stuff.

I wish I could tell him the truth. He'll have to take it all back if it turns out we've discovered priceless treasure.

## Monday November 20th

Mr Thompson the journalist spotted us at the temple today and came over to talk. He asked how the dig was going and I admitted I'd got ill and had to leave.

He whipped his notebook out and started quizzing me about how serious the illness was.

No doubt he was hoping it was something serious so he could write his story about the curse.

I told him it was just sunstroke, that everyone else was fine and that there was no stupid curse.

He kept questioning me about whether anyone had broken a bone, or dropped a rock on their foot, or fallen into a deep hole.

*Tell me all you know!*

Eventually he gave up and put his notebook away. It was all beginning to sound like a pathetic curse anyway. Tutankhamun can't be a very fearsome king if the best he can do from beyond the grave is make someone stub their toe.

I think I managed to put Mr Thompson off. Mr Carter specifically mentioned that he didn't want the press around, and I'd hate to be to blame for someone like Mr Thompson turning up.

*Friday November 24th*
Lord Carnarvon and Lady Evelyn will be arriving tomorrow. We're finally about to learn the truth. Fingers crossed.

# Chapter 6

## Wonderful things

## Saturday November 25th

Mr Carter was already at the site when I arrived just after dawn. I wasn't meant to arrive until nine, but I couldn't sleep, so I thought I might as well head over.

The debris had been cleared from the staircase again, and Mr Carter was staring at the doorway and taking notes. He showed me the seals bearing Tutankhamun's name and the area that had been disturbed and resealed.

I took photographs while we waited, trying not to use up too much film before we were even inside.

Lord Carnarvon and his daughter turned up after ten, and Mr Carter put his team to work on the doorway straight away. We stood back and shielded our noses as they struck down the wall of stone and plaster.

There was a narrow passage beyond, which sloped downwards. Unfortunately, it was completely filled with rubble. We weren't going to find out the truth just yet.

I expected Lord Carnarvon and Evelyn to settle back in the shade, but they kept peering at the passageway as our team carried the rocks away. Like us, they couldn't bear to look away in case they missed the moment we broke through.

Fragments of jars and painted pottery emerged along with the rubble. Mr Carter lined them up on the ground at the top of the stairs. A few

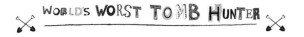

weeks ago, he'd have insisted each one was examined and catalogued before anyone moved, but he was as carried away as the rest of us now.

Soon a second blockage of stones and plaster appeared, which looked almost identical to the first. There were more seals, and once again they bore the name of Tutankhamun.

Mr Carter wanted me to photograph these new seals, but I said the light wasn't great at the bottom of the dingy passage. I offered to set up some electric lights if he gave me time, but Lord Carnarvon told us to stop wasting time and find out what was inside.

I could tell this was quite a dilemma for Mr Carter. He'd usually spend weeks writing notes about a sickle before touching it, and now he was being asked to destroy a wall of plaster covered

in ancient seals. On the other hand, the things inside would probably make the seals look about as interesting as a pile of camel vomit.

After staring at the wall for a few moments, he grabbed a pickaxe and tapped a hole in the upper left corner. I noticed his hands were trembling, and it took him quite a long time to do it.

He pulled away chunks of plaster and stone
before picking up a candle and peering through.

He was silent for a long moment, which seemed
to go on for ages. It was impossible to tell if he
was delighted or disappointed.

Lord Carnarvon asked him what he could see,
and Mr Carter simply said, 'Wonderful things.'

After that, I had to wait my turn. First Lord
Carnarvon peered inside with his eyes widening
and his moustache quivering. Then his daughter
took over, a huge grin spreading over her face.

Finally, I was handed the candle. In the
flickering light, I could make out the outlines
of statues, tables and chests. Everything in the
small room seemed to be coated in gold.

I know Mr Carter got into this archaeology business to unlock the secrets of the past and increase our knowledge of the ancient world, and he'd certainly done that. But this was something more. This was treasure. Gleaming, golden treasure that would make anyone awestruck, even if their knowledge of history only stretched back to the week before last.

Priceless artefacts that would each be the centrepiece of a grand museum were piled around like litter. I could see life-sized statues, lavishly decorated caskets and overturned chariots with golden wheels.

I turned around to see Mr Carter and Lord Carnarvon smiling and shaking hands. It might not have looked like much of a celebration, but for two stuffy English gentlemen, this was the equivalent of removing your shirt and running down the street while twirling it over your head.

Then Mr Carter grabbed my hand and thanked me for the idea of digging under the huts. I felt a huge sense of relief. Relief that these two men hadn't wasted all those decades, and relief that they'd remembered it was my idea.

Mr Carter returned to the hole for another look inside. After muttering to himself for a while, he announced he could see another doorway inside the room.

Lord Carnarvon asked Mr Carter what he was waiting for, and told him to get in there and see what was behind the next door.

This time Mr Carter wouldn't give in. He said we had to tackle our finds in an orderly way instead of just charging through. The tomb had waited three thousand years for us, so the least we could do was take our time over it.

Lord Carnarvon scowled. Someone as rich as him must be used to getting what he wants whenever he wants it. But Mr Carter was right. We're archaeologists, not tomb raiders, and we need to treat this extraordinary discovery with respect.

Mr Carter posted some of the team on guard for the night and we returned home to rest. I don't think I'll get much sleep tonight, and I doubt the others will get any at all.

## Sunday November 26th

This morning I set up the lights and photographed the seals. Then there was the agonising wait while the team carefully took down the layer of stones and plaster.

When this was done, we went in and examined the crazy jumble of chariot wheels, thrones, beds and sandals we'd glimpsed yesterday. The other doorway was to our right, and Mr Carter thinks this will be the burial chamber where Tutankhamun was laid to rest. He's calling the room we've discovered the 'antechamber'.

Mr Carter went around frantically examining things and scribbling notes. His handwriting was a messy scrawl and I doubt his jottings will be of much use. I think it was just his way of trying to take it all in.

I had to take as many photographs as I could without touching anything. Like Mr Carter I was flitting about with no real method, and I'll have to get Ibrahim's advice about getting proper light in the place.

Lord Carnarvon and Lady Evelyn came in
and gazed around too. Lord Carnarvon kept
reaching out to touch things, but Mr Carter had
to remind him how fragile everything was.

I was already beginning to wonder how I'd ever
manage to take pictures of everything when Mr
Carter shouted that he'd found a hole in the far
wall leading to yet another room.

It was also filled with ancient stuff, but this was the place the thieves had got to. They'd broken through to grab precious objects that would be easy to carry, leaving the rest strewn around the floor.

The things they'd casually cast aside would still be priceless to us, of course. But getting them safely out and sorting through them was going to be a headache.

Mr Carter's expression of awe was now replaced with one of worry. I think the amount of work we have to do was dawning on him. It will take months to safely preserve, remove and catalogue all of these new objects. Maybe even years.

This evening I went back to Ibrahim's darkroom to develop the shots I'd taken so far. I tried to describe how brilliant our find was, but it was hard to do it justice after such an exhausting day.

Ibrahim understood when he saw the pictures.

His eyes lit up as he saw the beautiful things we'd found. He reckons that selling the exclusive images to newspapers will make him as rich as Tutankhamun himself, and he began to list all the journalists he'd contacted. I had to snap my fingers in front of his eyes and tell him to keep things secret for now.

Mr Carter will hold an official tomb opening soon, but in the meantime he wants to get as much done as he can without unwanted attention.

Ibrahim agreed, and I had to make him promise over and over again not to tell anyone. He's not always brilliant at keeping things to himself.

When that was done, he ran around his house grabbing pieces of equipment that would help me take even better shots. He's even letting me use his best camera, which I'm not usually allowed to touch.

Maybe it's his way of admitting he was wrong about Mr Carter and the dig.

Mum and Dad were also pretty amazed when I showed them the pictures. Dad didn't even give me a lecture about how I should get a proper job like his. He just stared at the prints with wide eyes.

### Monday November 27th

Mr Carter announced he isn't going to open the door to the burial chamber until he's properly dealt with all the objects in the antechamber. Lord Carnarvon took out his pocket watch and asked Mr Carter how long that would take.

I think he was hoping Mr Carter might have it done by tomorrow, but it turns out he was talking about weeks or maybe even months.

Lord Carnarvon stormed out of the tomb, but Lady Evelyn hung around and tried to convince Mr Carter to at least let them have a little peek into the burial chamber.

Instead of being persuaded, Mr Carter launched into a big speech about how the finds weren't our property to treat as we pleased. He said we were merely the link between the ancients and future generations, and we couldn't risk losing even the smallest scrap of knowledge.

Lady Evelyn frowned and stomped off after her father. I think Mr Carter was so stressed about all the work ahead of us that he forgot he was speaking to someone much richer than him. In England this is as forbidden as going to church with no trousers on, and it wasn't long before he had to go out and apologise.

Lord Carnarvon and Evelyn have reluctantly agreed that his patient approach is correct, and they're going back to England while we sort out the antechamber.

They left for Luxor this afternoon, and Mr Carter went with them to organise the delivery of all the packing and preserving materials.

For the rest of the day I was alone in the tomb with my camera, and the strange atmosphere of the place almost overwhelmed me. I was surrounded by objects that hadn't been touched in three thousand years. It was enough to make my head spin.

# Chapter 7

# Mummy mania

## *Tuesday November 28*<sup>th</sup>

I was working in the tomb this morning when
I heard someone arguing with the guards. I
put my camera down and made my way up the
corridor. It wasn't long before I recognised the
voice. Ibrahim was here.

I dashed up the steps and told the guards to
let him through. That's when I noticed that he
wasn't alone. Mr Thompson was with him.

I felt like telling the guards to refuse Ibrahim
entry if he was going to bring that idiot with
him, but they both pushed through.

I asked Ibrahim why he hadn't managed to
keep the news to himself, and he said that
Mr Thompson had tricked him into revealing
the truth by asking questions until he let
something slip.

Hmm. I suspect what really happened was that Ibrahim got carried away with bragging and didn't remember it was meant to be a secret until too late.

There wasn't time to be angry with Ibrahim, however, as Mr Thompson pushed past me and strolled down the corridor to the antechamber.

That's how he became only the fifth person in modern times to see one of the most incredible discoveries ever. And the worst thing was that he didn't even seem impressed. He nodded and said we had some good stuff, as if he were browsing in a furniture shop.

I told him to leave, but he said he was going to report on what he'd seen anyway, and if I wanted it to be favourable I should let him stick around and speak to Mr Carter. I remembered all that nonsense about the curse, and realised I had no choice but to let him stay.

Mr Carter arrived an hour later, and seemed pretty flustered from his trip. This was quite lucky for me, because it meant he was too tired to get angry about Ibrahim and Mr Thompson.

He agreed to let Mr Thompson send a dispatch to *The Times* in London if he left us alone. Mr Thompson agreed, but kept asking questions as if Mr Carter had agreed to a full interview. I had to shove him up the steps to get rid of him. You'd think his silly idea about the curse would have made him want to leave quickly.

After Mr Thompson had gone, Mr Carter still had Ibrahim to deal with. He kept coming up with ways of lighting the antechamber that Mr Carter wouldn't agree to. He suggested using flashes, but Mr Carter thought this might damage things. Then he suggested using an elaborate system of mirrors to get the sunlight in, but Mr Carter wasn't having that either.

In the end, Mr Carter agreed to let Ibrahim bring two powerful electric lights. I can move these around to illuminate the objects one at a time, and with slow exposures I should get some very clear images.

Ibrahim also suggested that I should set up a darkroom in one of the empty tombs nearby. Mr Carter agreed, which I found surprising, as I was expecting him to say it was disrespectful. I think he just wanted to get rid of Ibrahim.

It's a pretty good arrangement for me, though. It means I just have to walk a short way up the valley every time I want to develop some prints, instead of going all the way back to Luxor.

I hope the old pharaoh doesn't come back to haunt me. Though I suppose if he did, I could end up with a photograph of a ghost, which would be pretty exciting.

## Wednesday November 29th

Mum and Dad have agreed to let me stay over at the site while we're working on the antechamber. They were a little worried about me sleeping in a deserted tomb at night, but I explained that Mr Carter is hiring guards, so if anything I'll be even safer than at home.

It will mean I can spend all my waking hours photographing the precious objects, and won't have to waste valuable energy getting across the river to the valley every day. It will also mean I can protect the tomb from any rival photographers who try to sneak in while I'm away.

I dragged my sleeping mat over to Ibrahim's house, and he's going to have it sent to the valley along with the new lights.

This afternoon we had the official tomb opening, which was attended by the governor and many other local officials. Word had obviously spread in Luxor, because a huge crowd came out to line the top of the pit, and our guards had to hold them back.

It's great that so many people came out for the

ceremony, but I hope they don't return. We need peace and quiet for our work, not a huge gathering of spectators.

## Thursday November 30th

If anything, the crowd has got even bigger. Mr Carter is worried about them stealing artefacts, so he's employing even more guards and fixing a steel gate to the entrance.

A number of other photographers have appeared, but Mr Carter is staying true to his word and refusing them entry. I helped to find the tomb, so it's only fair that I should have exclusive access. They can go and look for an exciting find of their own if they think it's unfair.

I have to pass a section of the crowd as I walk between Tutankhamun's tomb and my new darkroom. I often spot the other photographers taking shots of me, which shows how desperate they must be.

I was tempted to wrap myself in bandages and get the guards to carry me out on a stretcher just to get their hopes up. Then when they'd wasted enough film I'd leap up and laugh at them.

But I decided against it. They already hate me enough.

### Friday December 1st

I wish I hadn't put the idea of a mummy coming back to life in my head last night. Ibrahim delivered my sleeping mat and all the equipment in the evening, then went away as the sun was setting.

Mr Carter and his crew soon left too, and I was left alone in the dark tomb. I could see one of the guards patrolling in the distance, which should have made me feel safer. But I kept imagining he was the shuffling mummy of Tutankhamun, come back to life to seek revenge.

I don't know why this frightened me so much. I'm not the toughest person in town, but even I could win a fight against a crumbly old dead body. All you'd have to do is unwrap him and his legs would fall off.

When I finally got to sleep, I had a nightmare about the mummy cornering me and strangling me with his cloth hands. I woke up and found I'd managed to tangle myself in my turban.

Luckily I didn't strangle myself with it. Mr Thompson would have had a field day if I'd

been found dead in an ancient tomb so soon after disturbing Tutankhamun's eternal rest.

## *Monday December 4ᵗʰ*

Our crowds continue to grow. Some of the onlookers have turned on us now, and I thought it might be because we won't let them into the tomb. But Mr Carter explained the real reason. Apparently, my exclusive photographs and Mr Thompson's exclusive report have made all the other newspapers jealous, so they've been spreading rumours that we're going to load all the treasure into a plane, fly it back to London and sell it to rich collectors.

I went out to address the crowd and set matters straight this morning, but one of the photographers shouted that I was getting a cut of the profits and I was drowned out by boos.

**135**

Oh well. Let them think what they like. We have important work to do, and we'll have to get on with it whether we're getting cheered or jeered. It would be nicer to have no noise at all, though.

### Tuesday December 5th

Ibrahim visited today to pick up the prints, and he said he'd been besieged with newspapers who want my photographs.

Apparently, Mr Thompson's article has caused the world to break out in ancient Egypt fever, and we should expect an influx of tourists to join the onlookers soon.

Great. More noise and hassle is just what we need.

I suppose it's good that everyone is just as excited about these finds as we are, though. It would be worse if the news only made the fifth page of the newspapers, after someone rescuing a cat from a tree.

I led Ibrahim from Tutankhamun's tomb to the darkroom, and he loved walking past the other photographers. He's met some before, and made sure to stop and gloat at them. I told him to hurry up because he'd only make the rival newspapers angrier and more likely to make up lies, but he still sauntered past, waving and grinning.

No doubt tomorrow the newspapers will be claiming we've built a bonfire out of Tutankhamun's possessions.

## GET REAL

*The discovery of Tutankhamun's tomb in 1922 inspired a global frenzy that influenced art, film, music, fashion and even furniture. From the novelty song 'Old King Tut' to the horror film* The Mummy, *the impact of Mr Carter's find could be seen in many places in the 1920s and 1930s.*

## Wednesday December 6th

Mr Carter must have been impressed with my darkroom because he's decided to use another of the empty tombs as his laboratory. He's going to use it to examine the artefacts, treat them with preserving chemicals and pack them into crates. There's a cliff overhanging the entrance, which means I can photograph things without placing them in harmful sunlight. It's also well away from anywhere the other photographers can get to, so my exclusive shots won't be in any danger either.

*Thursday December 7th*

Mr Carter is now starting to remove the fragile objects. The problem is that so many of them are piled on top of each other that touching one brings the risk of sending the others crashing to the ground.

It's like that game where you make a pile of sticks and then try to pull one away without making the other sticks fall down. Except that if we lose, we'll damage something irreplaceable.

Mr Carter has built a system of wooden supports to hold everything in place, and he's gradually lifting and bandaging things onto stretchers so they can be carried over to the lab.

The crowd go wild whenever one of these stretchers goes past and the guards have to hold them back. The photographers always push forward, but all they'll get is blurry images of objects I've already shot without the bandages on. Good luck selling those to newspapers.

There are so many artefacts and they all need to be treated with care. I think it will be months before we've cleared them and we can finally open the door to the burial chamber.

Looks like I'll just have to be patient for a while longer.

## *Tuesday January 2nd*

We've made good progress on clearing the antechamber and the small room at the side, which we're now calling 'the annex'. But it seems our luck might be about to change.

The weather has turned and dark clouds are forming above us. A heavy storm could be on the way, and that would mean the tomb, the laboratory and even my darkroom would be flooded. All of our priceless artefacts would be destroyed.

Mr Carter is desperately trying to think of a way to get the contents of his lab to safety, but I think he knows there's not much he could do. A sudden flood would mean motorcars would be unable to get here and there would be nowhere for an aeroplane to land.

Maybe we'd just have to grab the best artefacts and run through the flood waters, desperately trying to get them to safety.

## Wednesday January 3rd

I was on my way from the tomb to the darkroom this morning when a British man jumped over the wall and made for the tomb entrance. He was carrying a large bag and I wondered what he was up to.

Mr Carter is very worried about people stealing from the tombs, but this man could hardly get away with it in front of such a large crowd. It's not like we'd have trouble finding witnesses.

It wasn't what he had in mind anyway. He stopped at the top of the steps, opened his bag and took out a book and a bottle. He propped the book open with one hand and read out some strange words while pouring liquid down the steps.

**143**

I asked him what he was doing, but he just kept saying the odd words. By this time, two of the guards had jogged down and Mr Carter had emerged from the tomb.

The man explained he was a worshipper of the god Horus. He believed that the rainclouds had been sent by Tutankhamun as punishment for disturbing his tomb and he was reading a spell from the Book of the Dead to banish them. The liquid was a mixture of milk, wine and honey that was part of the spell.

As the guards dragged the man away, he yelled that Tutankhamun was still very angry and suggested that Mr Carter employ him full-time to ward off other misfortunes.

I told him we were fine for spells, and he should try the other local businesses to see if they wanted any.

Mr Carter sighed and went back to the tomb, but I couldn't stop watching the strange man. Ibrahim clearly wasn't lying when he said Egypt mania was sweeping the world.

It just makes me glad Mr Thompson never ran his stupid story about the curse. There are obviously a lot of people out there willing to believe such nonsense.

## *GET REAL*

The Book of the Dead *is a collection of spells that the ancient Egyptians believed would help them after death. These were often written on papyrus sheets and placed inside tombs. The spells were translated and compiled as a book in the nineteenth century.*

## Thursday January 4ᵗʰ

The clouds broke in the early hours of this morning, but we had a lucky escape. Only a few drops fell on our valley, though we could see heavy rain in the distance.

On one hand, I'm relieved that our priceless finds haven't been ruined. On the other hand, I'm annoyed that the idiot from yesterday will think he's the one who saved us.

## Monday January 15ᵗʰ

As if we needed more evidence of our new fame, sacks of letters are now arriving. Mr Carter is ignoring them and leaving them to pile up in the laboratory, but I sometimes look through them. There are plenty that seem to be written by friends of our recent intruder, who

either claim to be passing on messages from Tutankhamun himself or suggest spells we should be using.

There are many asking how much our items cost as if we'd decided to open an antiques stall. One very confused British lady wrote to complain that she'd bought one of our dog figures from a street vendor and the gold leaf had rubbed away. It was hard to tell if she realised she'd bought a fake or she was complaining about the quality of workmanship three thousand years ago.

I found a letter offering hundreds of US dollars for the moving picture rights to our story and thought Mr Carter might be interested. It seemed like someone was offering us a lot of money for doing nothing, so I thought it was at least worth sharing. But he rejected the offer without taking his eyes off the chariot wheel he was examining. He said he'd seen one of those moving pictures once and it was ridiculous.

Maybe it was just as well. They'd only get some big star like Rudolph Valentino to play Mr Carter, and then we'd get even more fawning fans turning up.

### Tuesday January 23rd

Mr Carter doesn't think Tutankhamun was very old when he died. He keeps finding clothes in a child's size, and at first he thought he must have been buried with his old clothes. But now he's found some paintings where he looks really young.

Mr Carter reckons he might have been as young as nine when he took the throne. Having a king that age sounds very unwise to me. There must have been executions of teachers every week.

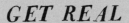

## GET REAL

*Tutankhamun was only about nine years old when he became king in around 1332 BC. A time of unrest had left the rest of the royal family dead, and he had to take over. Tutankhamun wasn't completely on his own, however. He had powerful advisors like Grand Vizier Ay, who became pharaoh when Tutankhamun died.*

### Friday February 16th

The antechamber is cleared now, and our precious finds are on their way to Cairo. It's finally time to open the burial chamber.

# Chapter 8
⊢——⊣
# The face of
the pharoah

## Saturday February 17th

I waited inside the empty antechamber and watched as Mr Carter chipped away at the blockage of plaster and stones. When he'd created a small hole, he stuck his torch in and peered through.

He whispered that he could see a wall of solid gold. I urged him to work quicker, so I could see it for myself. But he was worried about the loose stones damaging what was inside, so he continued at his usual snail's pace.

As the blockage came down, I got a look at the golden wall. It was actually one side of what looked like a huge shiny cupboard. Mr Carter said this was called a 'shrine' and Tutankhamun's tomb was inside it.

I asked if Tutankhamun had been a little on the chubby side to need such a massive coffin, but Mr Carter explained that pharaohs were buried inside many layers. There would be other shrines inside this one, then a stone coffin known as the 'sarcophagus', then three wooden coffins, with the mummified body of the king inside the final one.

When all the stones were gone, I followed Mr Carter into the narrow gap between the huge shrine and the wall. It was covered in paintings that I couldn't make out very well, but seemed to show some ancient Egyptians and animal-headed gods. I asked Mr Carter what they meant, and he said they showed Tutankhamun being welcomed into the afterlife by a goddess called Hathor and a god called Anubis.

I thought Mr Carter would have been fascinated by these figures, but he was already at the far end of the chamber and muttering

under his breath. I stepped carefully over to see what had grabbed his attention.

Mr Carter had found a doorway to yet another chamber, this one unblocked. He was staring at another golden shrine. This one was much smaller, and had goddess statues on each side.

He was so excited that his hand was shaking, and the light was jittering back and forth in the dark tomb. I asked him what the shrine was, and he replied in a fast whisper that was hard to follow. But from what I understood, he thinks the chest houses four 'canopic jars', which contained the liver, stomach, lungs and intestines of the pharaoh, all in tiny golden coffins.

I wondered what it must be like to be so rich that even your smelly intestines get their own golden coffin.

*156*

There were many other amazing objects in the new chamber, including model boats, ivory caskets and a large statue of the god Anubis. As with the antechamber it was all too much to take in. Mr Carter used to go crazy every time he found a scrap of pottery, now he had yet another room full of treasure. It must have been like going to a restaurant and being given everything from the menu at once.

We wandered back out of the tomb and Mr Carter picked up his notebook in a kind of daze. He scribbled in it before letting it fall to his lap and staring into the distance.

I leaned over and saw he'd just written the word 'gold' over and over again. He went home for a lie-down shortly afterwards.

## GET REAL

*Even the organs that were removed from the body were preserved during mummification. They were placed in four 'canopic jars', and stored in a chest near the coffin. Tutankhamun's canopic jars all feature his own face, but more often they had animal heads carved on them, representing the sons of the god Horus.*

## Sunday February 18th

I really want to open the shrines and see
Tutankhamun's mummy, but Mr Carter says it's
going to take a long time. Each shrine will have
to be carefully dismantled, examined and sent
to Cairo Museum. And with some of the sections
weighing half a tonne, it's not going to be easy.

In the meantime, I'm going to take my
electric lights around the burial chamber and
photograph the wall paintings. They're all
drawn in the same weird way where everyone's
bodies are facing forward but their heads are
facing sideways. I reckon everyone in ancient
Egypt would have had really bad neck ache if
that's how they went around.

They're amazingly bright and clear for
paintings that are three thousand years old.
Whoever did them must have known how to
mix paints that would last.

## GET REAL

*The ancient Egyptians decorated tomb walls with scenes of the new life that a pharaoh was beginning after death. The cool, dry conditions meant that many of them were wonderfully preserved.*

*The paints were made using natural minerals. The black would contain charcoal or soot. The red would contain ochre, a type of clay. The white would contain chalk. The green would contain powdered malachite. And the colour blue, which was very important to the ancient Egyptians, was made from heating silica, lime and copper.*

## Tuesday March 20<sup>th</sup>

Our work has been going slowly over the last few weeks, but now it's come to a complete standstill. Lord Carnarvon has been taken ill in Cairo and Mr Carter has gone to see him.

In the meantime, we're shutting down the dig. I'm going to abandon my darkroom here and go back to the old one in Ibrahim's house.

It's good that Mr Carter has gone to try to help Lord Carnarvon. After all, this discovery wouldn't have been possible if he hadn't paid for everything. But I really hope we can get back to the burial chamber soon. I can't wait to finally come face to face with Tutankhamun's mummy.

## Sunday April 8th

I don't really know how to write this, so I'll just come out with it. Mr Carter returned from Cairo today with terrible news. Lord Carnarvon is dead. It seems he was bitten by a mosquito, and accidentally cut the bite while shaving. The cut became infected, and he got blood poisoning, which developed into pneumonia. He died in the early hours of Thursday morning, and his body is now on the way to England for burial.

I only met him a few times, so it isn't like losing a close friend, but I'm still in shock. Mr Carter looks dazed. Even though he used to argue with Lord Carnarvon quite a lot, they'd worked together for years and I think they were fond of each other in their way.

I expect he also feels guilty that Lord Carnarvon never got to see Tutankhamun's mummy. If he'd known this was going to

happen he might not have been so strict about taking so much time.

## *Tuesday April 10ᵗʰ*

I've been in such a state of shock about Lord Carnarvon's death it didn't even cross my mind that this would happen.

Mr Carter called round to Ibrahim's house this afternoon and threw a newspaper down at my feet. He looked angry, and when I asked him what was wrong, he just jabbed his finger down at the paper.

It was a copy of *The Times*, and they were leading with the news of Lord Carnarvon's death. Underneath the main article was one suggesting that Lord Carnarvon had been killed by 'the curse of Tutankhamun'. My heart sank when I saw who had written it.

Mr Thompson.

Even though we'd given him an exclusive story to stop him printing this rubbish, he'd gone ahead anyway. Lord Carnarvon's death had obviously made it impossible to resist.

I scanned through the article and felt my pulse quicken. Mr Thompson had quoted the things

I'd said months ago about feeling cursed. He went on to claim that Tutankhamun's coffin was engraved with a spell bringing bad luck to anyone who disturbed it. He even suggested that Tutankhamun's freshly-opened tomb might have contained some sort of mysterious poison that had killed Lord Carnarvon, though there was no attempt to explain why the rest of us were fine.

I was about to tell Mr Carter that I hadn't really said any of it when I saw him storming away down the street.

This is awful. Now Mr Carter thinks I've been blabbing nonsense to newspapers less than a week after Lord Carnarvon's death. I'd be surprised if he ever lets me into the tomb again.

## Wednesday April II*th*

I trekked out to the site early this morning and found Mr Carter at work in his lab. He wouldn't speak to me at first, but I eventually managed to explain how the curse was all Mr Thompson's invention.

Mr Carter says he hopes the public don't take to the story, because then we'll be overrun by idiots like that man who poured the wine mixture down the steps.

I hope so too, but something tells me the interest is only going to grow. Everyone was already excited by the idea of us finding an Aladdin's cave of treasure under the ground. Now we have this tragic twist, it's going to get even worse.

## Tuesday April 17<sup>th</sup>

Much as I expected, this curse story is getting out of control. Famous people have joined in now, including Sir Arthur Conan Doyle, who writes the Sherlock Holmes stories. He believes that Lord Carnarvon was killed by a mysterious magical being known as an 'elemental'.

No, he wasn't. Mr Carter has spent his life recording every tiny scrap of flint and pottery he's seen in the ground. I think he'd have noticed if some sort of evil fairy had flown out and murdered Lord Carnarvon.

I read some of the Sherlock Holmes stories when I was in school. They were about an incredibly clever man. So how can they have been written by someone so silly he thinks that evil beings are a better explanation for Lord Carnarvon's death than blood poisoning? That's the biggest mystery of all.

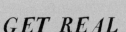

## GET REAL

*In his lifetime, Sir Arthur Conan Doyle was as famous for his spiritual beliefs as for his Sherlock Holmes stories. He believed it was possible for people to send their thoughts to others and to contact the dead. Conan Doyle was even tricked into believing fairies had been photographed. He claimed that Lord Carnarvon was killed by an ancient curse, giving credibility to a far-fetched story that was invented to sell newspapers.*

## Monday April 23rd

Still the curse story goes on. The newspapers are reporting that the lights went out all over Cairo at the exact time of Lord Carnarvon's death. Spooky, eh? Not really. The lights go out in Cairo all the time, and Tutankhamun died a few centuries too early to know what an electric light was, so I'd doubt he'd have known how to turn them off.

There are claims that Mr Carter's pet canary was eaten by a snake, that Lord Carnarvon's three-legged dog dropped dead at the same time he did, and that jackals resembling the god Anubis have been spotted near the tomb.

Really? Because Anubis has the body of a man and the head of a jackal in the pictures I've seen. If something like that had turned up, it would be a much bigger story than the tomb itself.

Just as I feared, our tragedy has brought even more unwelcome visitors. The crowds around the wall are so deep it feels like we're performing our work in a theatre.

Every time I walk past the crowd to my darkroom they surge forward and stare at me. Before they just wanted a glimpse of our treasures. Now they want to see the curse in action too.

A few days ago, I tripped over a rock to gasps of excitement. There were murmurs of disappointment when I got up again instead of being torn apart by angry jackal-headed beings. I almost felt like I should have apologised.

I'm just going to have to get used to all this nonsense. The newspapers seem to be having a competition to see who can go furthest, and these ghoulish onlookers will be around for a long time to come.

170

## GET REAL

*There were no curses written anywhere on Tutankhamun's tomb, but this didn't stop the idea from catching on. Every time someone associated with the discovery died, it was blamed on the 'mummy's curse'. The myth lives on to this day, even though most people involved lived into old age. Lady Evelyn, for example, died in 1980 at the age of 79.*

## Thursday April 26<sup>th</sup>

The outer shrine has now been cleared away, revealing a smaller one, also made of heavy sections of wood covered in gold leaf. Mr Carter's team is dismantling this new shrine while he makes a close examination of the walls.

He says the paintings look rushed, and also that the room itself is a little too small for a king's burial place. He believes it was actually intended for someone else, but it had to be used for Tutankhamun when he died unexpectedly.

This made me come up with the idea that Tutankhamun was murdered, and his body was hurried into this cramped tomb to keep it secret. Mr Carter wasn't very impressed with my idea. He said that archaeologists should carefully consider evidence instead of jumping to dramatic conclusions, or we'd be just as silly as the idiots who believe in curses.

I think he's just jealous because I've uncovered an ancient murder. I'm like Sherlock Holmes, except I solve mysteries three thousand years too late, and I wasn't created by someone who believes in evil fairies.

## *GET REAL*

*Tutankhamun's cause of death has never been identified, leading some to speculate that he was murdered. However, it's much more likely that his death was due to accident or illness. For example, scientists have found evidence he had malaria.*

*So if he wasn't murdered, why was his burial hurried? Again, we don't really know, but a few ideas have been put forward. For example, it might be that Tutankhamun's guardian Ay wanted to bury him quickly so he could take over as pharaoh before his rivals could mount a challenge.*

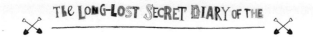

## Tuesday May 8<sup>th</sup>

Inside the second shrine we found a third shrine. And inside the third one we found, wait for it, you'll never guess... another shrine. At the moment it feels as if we'll keep finding smaller and smaller ones until we finally discover that this was just the tomb of Tutankhamun's pet flea. But Mr Carter assures me we're at the innermost shrine now.

## Wednesday May 9<sup>th</sup>

Mr Carter drew back the doors of the shrine to reveal a chunk of carved rock he calls the 'sarcophagus'. It's intact, with its lid still in place, but we can't just open it. It's very heavy and incredibly fragile, so Mr Carter's trying to think of a way to safely remove it. I suggested going into town and getting the strongest-looking men we could find to lift a corner each, but I think he wants something more scientific.

## *Wednesday May 23rd*

This was it. The day I finally met Tutankhamun.

Mr Carter managed to open the sarcophagus by rigging up a system of pulleys that let us lift the lid as one piece.

I watched from a safe distance as the ropes tightened and the lid rose. I was tempted to stick my head in and have a look, but I was worried the ropes might snap. I'd hate to have left this world knowing I was fuelling the curse story even more.

Eventually the lid rose, revealing a dark shroud covering a large shape. It seemed too chunky to be Tutankhamun's mummy, unless they'd gone overboard with the bandages.

Mr Carter reached in and pulled the shroud aside.

The thing underneath was a coffin, but it looked like no coffin I'd ever seen before.

Like the shrines, it was made of wood that was painted gold. There was a face on it too, which I guessed was meant to be Tutankhamun himself. He was wearing a large striped headdress and had a relaxed expression on his face, despite having a snake and vulture on his head. Jewels were set into the coffin, and they glinted as Mr Carter examined them with an electric light.

I watched as Mr Carter carefully removed the pins that fixed the lid in place. When he'd done this, he lifted it to reveal another coffin, also painted gold, and also covered in jewels.

Inside this coffin was an even smaller one.
At first I thought it was black, but Mr Carter
rubbed it with a cloth and revealed a bright,
shiny streak.

This coffin wasn't painted wood like the others.
It was solid gold. Mr Carter explained that the
black layer was probably caused by liquids that
had been used during the burial ceremony.

We had discovered a lot of precious things in
the tomb, but an entire coffin made of gold had
to be the most valuable yet.

Yet an even more amazing find was to come.

A solemn mood fell over us as Mr Carter
unfixed the top of the final coffin. This was
it. The climax of years of searching and
months of work. We were finally going to
see Tutankhamun himself.

Mr Carter lifted the lid and I found myself gasping.

Tutankhamun's small, mummified body was in there. The bandages were black and looked like they'd been treated with the same gooey liquid that had coated the gold coffin.

But it wasn't the body I was looking at. It was the mask covering Tutankhamun's head and shoulders.

Like the coffin, it was made of solid gold. The face was similar to the ones on the coffins, with the headdress, and the figures of the cobra and vulture.

It was beautifully crafted, and so lifelike that it really felt like we were coming face to face with the old pharaoh himself. It was hard to tear my eyes away from the mask, but I had to go and

get my camera. This extraordinary sight needed
to be recorded straight away.

As I looked in the viewfinder, I knew at once
I was capturing an image that would become
famous around the world.

## Thursday May 24th

Mr Carter is dismantling the tombs to send
to the Cairo Museum now. He went out to his
laboratory this morning, and I took the chance
to go back into the tomb and look at the death
mask on my own.

When I was there, I had a weird memory.
That day when I forgot to drink water, I
thought I saw a golden face appear in front of
me. It looked a lot like the mask.

Then I wondered if, far from cursing anyone who disturbed his rest, Tutankhamun wanted to be found. That he called me to his cramped tomb so he could be discovered and remembered.

It's probably not true. I think I just had a funny turn because I didn't have enough water. But I like the idea.

## Tuesday 29ᵗʰ May

My photographs of Tutankhamun's coffin and mask have been published all over the world and they've brought even more visitors flocking to us. If they're hoping to see the golden artefacts, they'll be disappointed. They're still in the tomb, which is strictly out of bounds. It doesn't seem to put off the crowds, though. Maybe just being near is enough for them.

I was gazing up at the mob with Mr Carter today when he said the real curse of Tutankhamun isn't bad-luck spells or anything silly like that, but all those people who won't leave us alone. He said the spectators had turned him from an archaeologist into a circus act.

I said we couldn't really blame the world for getting excited about Tutankhamun. All of humanity was waiting for some good news after the Great War and the Spanish Flu. And who could resist a story filled with adventure, mystery, tragedy and buried treasure?

Everyone knows about Tutankhamun now. And soon his wonderful artefacts will be on display for all to see.

Tutankhamun might not have lasted too long on the throne, but thanks to us, he's king again.

*The End*

## Tutankhamun and Howard Carter

The story of one of the most remarkable discoveries in history is really the story of two men who were born over 3,000 years apart – Tutankhamun and Howard Carter.

Tutankhamun was born around 1341 BC, and became king when he was about nine years old.

He ruled in a time of great change. His father Akhenaten had made himself deeply unpopular by trying to make the sun-god Aten the chief god.

Tutankhamun was soon the only surviving member of the royal family, and had to take the throne while still a young boy.

But it's thought that many of the important decisions would have been made by his guardian, who was called Ay.

Tutankhamun died just a few years later at the age of 18 or 19. No one knows for sure how he died, and this has led some people to believe he was murdered. Ay took over as pharaoh, so did he assassinate the young king to take the throne? Probably not. Scientists now think it's more likely that Tutankhamun died of an accident or a disease such as malaria.

By Tutankhamun's time, pyramids were no longer used for burial because they were hard to defend against robbers.

Instead, tombs were cut deep into the rock near the River Nile, in an area that became known as the 'Valley of the Kings'.

The tomb Tutankhamun was buried in was quite small, and might have been intended for someone else before his sudden death.

So how did a pharaoh who ruled for such a short time and died so young become so famous? It's all because of Howard Carter.

Howard Carter was born in London in 1874. He had a talent for art, and travelled to Egypt to copy tomb decorations when he was just 17.

He became fascinated with excavations, and found work with people like Theodore Davis.

In 1907, Theodore Davis found a small site which he believed was the tomb of Tutankhamun. He declared that all the important tombs in the Valley of the Kings had been discovered, but Carter didn't agree.

Funded by the English aristocrat Lord Carnarvon, he dedicated years of his life to finding the tomb of Tutankhamun. He finally succeeded in 1922, after clearing away a row of ancient workmen's huts.

The find captured the imagination of people all around the world and sparked a craze for ancient Egypt.

# How do we know about ancient Egypt?

Archaeologists study clues left by people in the past. There are many different types of archaeologist. Those who specialise in the study of ancient Egypt, like Howard Carter, are known as 'Egyptologists'.

Egyptologists find out about the past by examining objects, written records and buildings. Ancient Egypt is a very rich period to study, thanks to the vast amount of material that has survived.

Great treasure troves of statues, jewellery and weapons have been discovered.

Pharaohs like Tutankhamun were buried with valuable objects it was thought they'd need in the afterlife.

Most tombs were cleared out by ancient thieves, but a few were left for people like Howard Carter to find thousands of years later.

And many great monuments built by the ancient Egyptians have survived. The pyramids of Giza near Cairo are the most famous. The largest of these, the Great Pyramid, is the only one of the Seven Wonders of the Ancient World that is still standing today.

## Timeline

### c. 1341 BC

Tutankhamun is born. He is the son of the pharaoh Akhenaten, who has caused unrest with his worship of the sun-god Aten.

### c. 1332 BC

Tutankhamun becomes pharaoh following a period of turmoil that has left the rest of the royal family dead.

### c. 1323 BC

Tutankhamun dies, and is buried in a tomb cut deep into the rock in the Valley of Kings. His guardian Ay takes over as pharaoh. There now follows a gap of over 3,000 years in the story. Loads of great stuff happens like the rise and fall of the Roman empire, the middle ages and the invention of chocolate, but things stay pretty quiet inside the tomb.

## *Timeline*

*1874*

Howard Carter is born in London.

*1891*

Howard Carter travels to Egypt for the first time and becomes fascinated with tomb excavations.

*1907*

Theodore Davis finds a pit in the Valley of the Kings containing some large sealed storage jars. One of the jars contains a scrap of linen with Tutankhamun's name on it, and he mistakenly believes he's discovered Tutankhamun's tomb.

*1907*

The English aristocrat Lord Carnarvon employs Howard Carter to supervise the excavation of tombs near Luxor.

## Timeline

### 1912

Theodore Davis declares that the Valley of the Kings is now 'exhausted'. He soon gives up the right to excavate there.

### 1914

Howard Carter and Lord Carnarvon are awarded the right to dig in the Valley of the Kings.

### 1922

Howard Carter has a row of workmen's huts dismantled so he can search underneath. After years of unsuccessful searching, he finally finds the tomb of Tutankhamun.

### 1923

Lord Carnarvon suffers blood poisoning and pneumonia, and dies on April 5th. The idea that he was killed by the 'curse of Tutankhamun' captures the imagination of the public.

### 192

## *Timeline*

### *1930*

Howard Carter finally finishes clearing, preserving and cataloguing the contents of Tutankhamun's tomb. He spends his remaining years working as an agent for museums, and delivering lectures in Europe and the USA.

### *1932*

Hollywood cashes in on the craze for ancient Egyptian curses with the horror movie *The Mummy*. It spawns a franchise which survives to this day, with sequels, reboots and theme-park rollercoasters.

### *1939*

Howard Carter dies in London at the age of 64.

### *1980*

Lord Carnarvon's daughter Evelyn dies in London at the age of 79. Like many of the

## Timeline

people involved in the finding of the tomb of
Tutankhamun, she has survived into old age,
despite the so-called 'curse'.

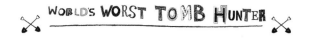
## Ancient Egypt Hall of Fame

### Akhenaten

Pharaoh who ruled from around 1352 BC until 1336 BC and was the father of Tutankhamun. He changed his name from Amenhotep IV to Akhenaten to show his devotion to the sun-god Aten. His religious ideas caused trouble, which continued into the reign of Tutankhamun.

### Cleopatra VII

The last pharaoh of Egypt, who ruled from 51 BC to 30 BC. She killed herself after losing the Battle of Actium. She lived closer to the time of the invention of the iPhone than the building of the Great Pyramid of Giza, which should give you an idea of how long the period we call 'ancient Egypt' really was.

### Howard Carter

English archaeologist who discovered Tutankhamun's tomb in 1922, sparking a worldwide craze about ancient Egypt.

## Ancient Egypt Hall of Fame

### Khufu

Pharaoh who reigned from 2589 BC to 2566 BC, according to some sources. Not much is known about him, but his name lives on forever because the Great Pyramid of Giza was built for him.

### Lord Carnarvon

English aristocrat who funded Howard Carter's search for Tutankhamun's tomb. His death in 1923 led to the myth of the 'mummy's curse'.

### Menes

The first pharaoh of Egypt, who united the upper and lower parts of the country and ruled in around 3100 BC. At least, that's what some historians believe. There isn't a lot of evidence about him, and historians don't agree on how to interpret it.

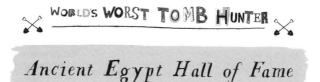
## Ancient Egypt Hall of Fame

### Ramesses II

Pharaoh who reigned from 1279 BC to 1213 BC and was known as Ramesses the Great. He built more monuments and statues than any other Egyptian king, and was portrayed as a brave warrior in paintings. His tireless self-promotion paid off, and he was remembered as a mighty and fearless leader.

### Theodore Davis

American lawyer who funded excavations in the Valley of the Kings between 1902 and 1914 and worked with Howard Carter and other archaeologists. Over thirty tombs were discovered in his name. He died in 1915, seven years before the eventual discovery of Tutankhamun's tomb.

## Ancient Egypt Hall of Fame

*Thutmose III*

Pharaoh who reigned between 1479 BC and 1425 BC. He was known as a fearless military leader, and created the largest empire of any ancient Egyptian king.

*Tutankhamun*

Young pharaoh who ruled from around 1332 BC to 1323 BC. He died while still a teenager and was buried in a small tomb probably intended for someone else. But when Howard Carter discovered his tomb in 1922, he became the most famous pharaoh of all. He was even given the affectionate nickname 'King Tut'.

## Glossary

**Canopic jar**
Container used for storing the stomach, intestines, liver and lungs of someone who's died. At least, I hope they've died. If they haven't, they might want to have their innards back.

**Darkroom** A room sealed off from natural light, used for developing photographs.

**Antechamber** A small room that leads to a bigger one.

**Archaeologist** Someone who studies history through examining objects from the past.

**Egyptologist** An archaeologist who studies ancient Egypt.

**Embalming** The process of treating a dead body to stop it from rotting.

**Artefact** A human-made object from a period in the past.

# Glossary

**Excavation**
A site where objects or remains from the past are uncovered. Also known as a 'dig'.

**Great War**
The name given to the First World War at the time. The term we use now only became standard after the Second World War broke out.

**Hieroglyph** A small picture representing a sound or idea. The ancient Egyptians combined these into a system of writing known as 'hieroglyphics'.

**Intact**
Something that is undamaged. In the case of ancient tombs, it means one that was never raided and emptied by thieves.

**Monument**
A statue or building built to remember a person or event.

**Mummification**
The process of preserving the remains of a person or animal. It was very expensive, so only the royal family and the very rich got to become mummies after death.

## Glossary

**Mummy**
The preserved body of a dead person or animal. Mummies have inspired a lot more horror movies than other archaeological finds. For example, no one has yet made a film about scrolls rising from the earth to seek bloody revenge.

**Papyrus**
The name of a plant that grows in the Nile valley, and also the sheets made from it that were written on. Our word 'paper' is derived from it.

**Pharaoh**
The title given to a ruler in ancient Egypt.

**Pyramid**
A giant stone tomb with a square base and four triangular sloping sides that meet in a point at the top.

**Sarcophagus**
A stone coffin that was often covered in carvings. It could contain further wooden coffins, as in the case of Tutankhamun.

## Glossary

**Scribe**
People who kept a written record of life in ancient Egypt. It's partly thanks to the scribes that we know so much about the era.

**Shrine** A container for the remains of a dead person. The term is also used more generally to refer to a place associated with someone holy.

**Spanish Flu** The deadly flu outbreak following the end of the First World War that is thought to have killed an estimated 25 million people.

**Thebes** An ancient Egyptian city located east of the Nile. Its ruins are within the modern city of Luxor.

**Vizier** The chief advisor to the pharaoh in the ancient Egyptian government.

# THE LONG-LOST SECRET DIARY OF THE WORLD'S WORST

Shortlisted for the
Lancashire School Library Service
Fantastic Book Awards (FBA) 2017–18.

'Although easy to read, the vocabulary is
great and the plot lines engaging – excellent
reads for developing readers.'
Library Girl and Book Boy Blog

Tim Collins / Sarah Horne

PB ISBN: 978-1-912233-19-9

Tim Collins/ Sarah Horne

PB ISBN: 978-1-912233-20-5

Tim Collins / Isobel Lundie

PB ISBN: 978-1-912537-26-6

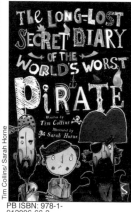

Tim Collins / Sarah Horne

PB ISBN: 978-1-912006-67-0

Tim Collins/ Sarah Horne

PB ISBN: 978-1-912006-66-3

# A selected list of Scribo titles

The prices shown below are correct at the time of going to press. However, The Salariya Book Company reserves the right to show new retail prices on covers, which may differ from those previously advertised.

---

**Gladiator School** by Dan Scott

| | | | |
|---|---|---|---|
| 1 | Blood Oath | 978-1-908177-48-3 | £6.99 |
| 2 | Blood & Fire | 978-1-908973-60-3 | £6.99 |
| 3 | Blood & Sand | 978-1-909645-16-5 | £6.99 |
| 4 | Blood Vengeance | 978-1-909645-62-2 | £6.99 |
| 5 | Blood & Thunder | 978-1-910184-20-2 | £6.99 |
| 6 | Blood Justice | 978-1-910184-43-1 | £6.99 |

**Iron Sky** by Alex Woolf

| | | | |
|---|---|---|---|
| 1 | Dread Eagle | 978-1-909645-00-4 | £9.99 |
| 2 | Call of the Phoenix | 978-1-910184-87-5 | £6.99 |

**Children of the Nile** by Alain Surget

| | | | |
|---|---|---|---|
| 1 | Cleopatra must be Saved! | 978-1-907184-73-4 | £5.99 |
| 2 | Caesar, Who's he? | 978-1-907184-74-1 | £5.99 |
| 3 | Prisoners in the Pyramid | 978-1-909645-59-2 | £5.99 |
| 4 | Danger at the Circus! | 978-1-909645-60-8 | £5.99 |

**Ballet School** by Fiona Macdonald
1. Peter & The Wolf      978-1-911242-37-6  £6.99
2. Samira's Garden      978-1-912006-62-5  £6.99

**Aldo Moon** by Alex Woolf
1 Aldo Moon and the Ghost
   at Gravewood Hall      978-1-908177-84-1  £6.99

**The Shakespeare Plot** by Alex Woolf
1 Assassin's Code      978-1-911242-38-3  £9.99
2 The Dark Forest      978-1-912006-95-3  £9.99
3 The Powder Treason      978-1-912006-33-5  £9.99

---

Visit our website at:

# www.salariya.com

All Scribo and Salariya Book Company titles can be ordered from your local bookshop, or by post from:

The Salariya Book Co. Ltd,
25 Marlborough Place
Brighton
BN1 1UB